This Igloo book belongs to:

. . . .

. . . .

Reading Together

This story is written in a special way so that a child and an adult can 'take turns' in reading the text.

The Queen sent Snow White out into the woods with a huntsman.
The Queen told the huntsman to kill Snow White. But the huntsman felt sorry for Snow White. He did not kill her.
The huntsman let Snow White run away.

The huntsman let Snow White run away.

The left hand side is for the adult to read.

The right hand side has a simple sentence (taken from the story) which the child reads.

Firstly, it is always helpful to read the whole book to your child, stopping to talk about the pictures. Explain that you are going to read it again but this time the child can join in.

Read the left hand page and when you come to the sentence which is repeated on the other page run your finger under this. Your child then tries to read the same sentence opposite.

Searching for the child's sentence in the adult version is a useful activity. Your child will have a real sense of achievement when all the sentences on the right hand page can be read. Giving lots of praise is very important.

Enjoy the story together.

I Can Read...

Snow White

Once upon a time there was
a beautiful girl called Snow White.
Her father was the King and her
stepmother was the Queen.
The Queen had a magic mirror.

The Queen had a magic mirror.

Every day, the Queen looked in the
mirror and said,
"Mirror Mirror on the wall, who is the
fairest of them all?"
Every day the mirror replied,
"You are the fairest of them all."
But one day the magic mirror said,
"Snow White is the fairest of them all."
The Queen was very angry.

The Queen was very angry.

The Queen sent Snow White out into the woods with a huntsman.
The Queen told the huntsman to kill Snow White. But the huntsman felt sorry for Snow White. He did not kill her.
The huntsman let Snow White run away.

The huntsman let Snow White
run away.

Snow White ran into the woods.
She found a little house.
Snow White went into the house.
Inside there were seven little beds.
Snow White fell asleep on one of the beds.
When Snow White woke up she saw
seven dwarves.

Snow White fell asleep on one of the beds.

The dwarves said, "This is our house.
What are you doing here?"
"I am frightened," said Snow White.
Snow White asked the dwarves to
help her.
The dwarves said that Snow White could
live in their house.
They all lived happily together.

Snow White asked the dwarves
to help her.

The Queen thought Snow White
was dead.
She said, "Mirror mirror on the wall,
who is the fairest of them all?"
The magic mirror said, "Snow White
is still the fairest of them all!"
The Queen was very angry.

The Queen thought Snow White was dead.

The Queen put a magic spell on an apple.
The Queen dressed up as an old lady.
She went into the woods.
She knocked on the door of the little house.
Snow White opened the door.

The Queen put a magic spell
on an apple.

The Queen gave the apple to Snow White.
Snow White bit the apple. She fell down.
It was as if she was dead.
The Queen was very happy.

The Queen gave the apple to Snow White.

The dwarves put Snow White into
a glass coffin.
One day a handsome Prince rode by.
The Prince thought Snow White was
very beautiful.
The Prince kissed Snow White.

The Prince kissed Snow White.

Snow White woke up.
She was not dead after all.
The wicked Queen ran away and was
never seen again.
Snow White and the Prince lived happily
ever after. So did the seven dwarves.

Snow White woke up.

Key Words

Can you read these words and find them in the book?

Snow White

apple

King

Queen

dwarves

Questions and Answers

Now that you've read the story can you answer these questions?

a. Who had a magic mirror?

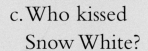

b. What kind of fruit did the Queen put a spell on?

c. Who kissed Snow White?

Tell your own Story

Can you make up a different story
with the pictures and words below?

horse

mirror

run

cottage

dwarves

Queen

King

woods

Mix and Match

Draw a line from the pictures to the correct word to match them up.

King

mirror

Queen

Snow White

dwarves

apple